ANIMALOGIES

A Collection of Animal Analogies

Written and illustrated by fourth-grade students of
Six to Six Interdistrict Magnet School
Cooperative Educational Services in Bridgeport, Connecticut

This book is dedicated to the fourth grade authors from Reseda, California whose book, *Who Let the Cat Out of the Bag?*, not only let us know about the *Kids Are Authors* competition, but inspired us, as well.

Copyright © 2003 by Scholastic Inc
Scholastic and associated logos are trademarks and/or registered trademarks of Scholastic Inc
ISBN 0-439-61173-3 ·

12 11 10 9 8 7 6 5 4 3 2 1   00 01 02 03 04

Book Design by Bill Henderson
Printed and bound in the U.S.A.

First Printing, July 2003

Squawk is to crow

SQUAWK

as squeak is to ...

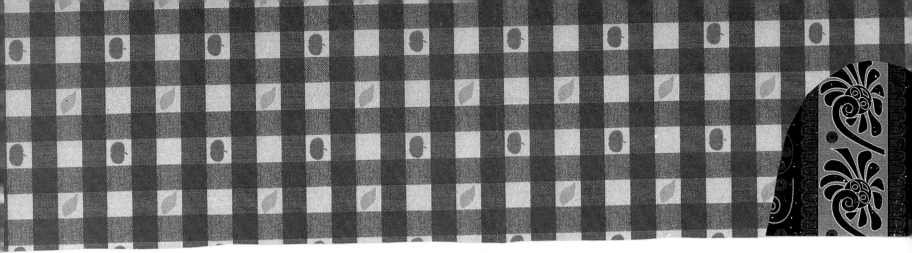

4

SQUEAK

mouse!

Jump is to kangaroo

5

as run is to ...

cheetah!

Feather is to bird

as scale is to ...

snake!

Colt is to horse

as tadpole is to ...

frog!

White is to polar bear

as pink is to ...

pig!

Fly is to butterfly

as dig is to ...

earthworm!

Blowhole is to whale

as trunk is to ...

elephant!

Desert is to iguana

as ocean is to ...

octopus!

Tiny is to ant

as humongous is to ...

hippopotamus!

Furry is to dog

as slimy is to ...

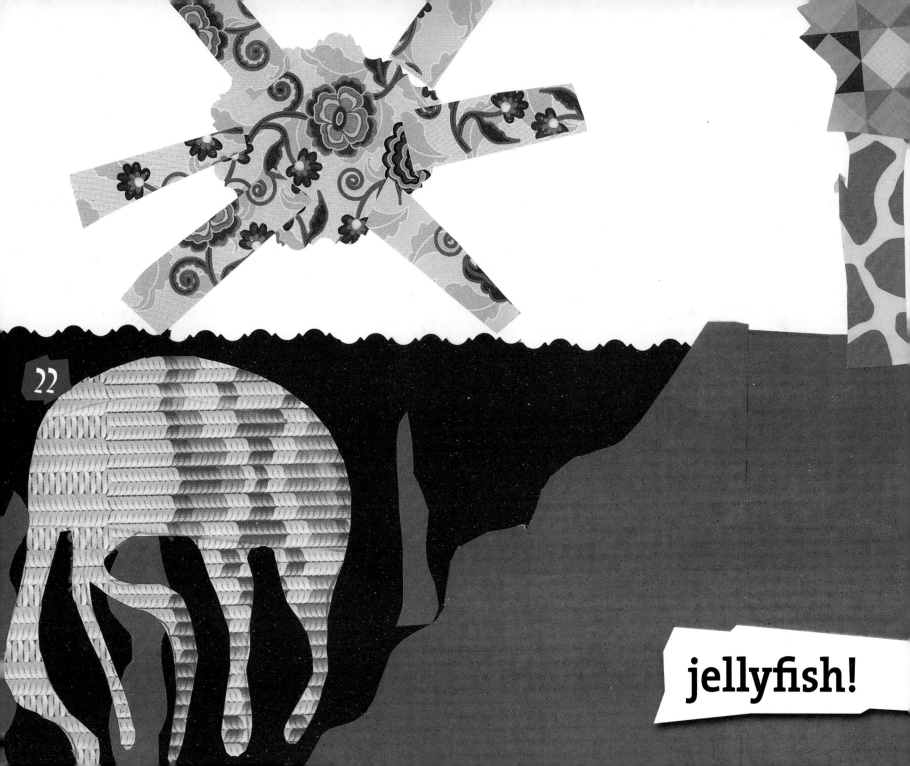

jellyfish!

Paw is to tiger

as claw is to ...

Kid is to goat

as cub is to ...

Smooth is to dolphin

as soft is to ...

cat!

Roar is to lion

as talk is to ...

parrot!

Front row, left to right: Despina Filippakis, Justina Matos, Caroline Proto, Jessica Gomes, Bennett Williamson, Kyle Faria-Robertson, Cory Steer

Back row, left to right: Andressa Galvao, Melinda Freund, Mrs. Kathy Brody, Clement Eneh, Julia Mateusiak, Justin Kirnon, Chase Carbone, Danny Rodriguez, Christopher Zamot, Danielle Rooney, Mrs. Lynn Walytok

Kids Are Authors ®
Books written by children for children

The Kids Are Authors ® Competition was established in 1986 to encourage children
to read and to become involved in the creative process of writing.
Since then, thousands of children have written and illustrated books as participants
in the Kids Are Authors ® Competition. The winning books in the annual competition
are published by Scholastic Inc. and are distributed by Scholastic Book Fairs throughout the
United States.

For more information:
Kids Are Authors®
1080 Greenwood Blvd.
Lake Mary, FL 32746

Or visit our web site at:
www.scholastic.com/kidsareauthors